IGNATIUS
OF LOYOLA
and His
Wise Horse

Written and Illustrated by
BY HAYLEY MEDEIROS

CARITAS PRESS

IGNATIUS
OF LOYOLA
and His
Wise Horse

Written and Illustrated by
BY HAYLEY MEDEIROS

CARITAS PRESS

Ignatius of Loyola and His Wise Horse
Copyright © 2020 Hayley Medeiros
Printed in the USA

First Edition
10 9 8 7 6 5 4 3 2 1
ISBN 978-1-940209-39-5

Contact Sherry@LilyTrilogy.com

Dedicated in loving memory of
Sister Gabrielle Marry, IBVM
and Monsignor Michael O'Grady

Monsignor Mike and Sister Gabby delight in singing "Molly Malone" with Annie Behrendt, one of many students at Ss. Simon & Jude School in Phoenix who benefitted from Father Mike's and Sister Gabby's zeal for Irish folk songs. Photo courtesy of the Behrendt family. Used by permission.

"Blessed are the pure in heart,
for they shall see God."
(Matthew 5:8)

Many centuries ago, in the castle of Loyola in northern Spain, a noble boy was born and baptized with the name of Iñigo, although he later came to call himself Ignatius. As Ignatius grew, his father thought his noble son would be well-suited to a life at court. So he sent him away to be a royal page boy in the household of a nobleman affiliated with Ferdinand, King of Castile. There Ignatius worked and was educated in all of the chivalrous arts. He learned fine manners, how to dress, how to speak and write eloquently, horsemanship, armed combat, and the art of wooing a highborn lady.

As a young man, Ignatius quickly acquired a great reputation as a brave, honorable soldier. His handsome appearance, charming manners, and the renown earned by his knightly exploits made him a favorite in high society and at court. Ignatius enjoyed many of the vain pleasures the world had to offer a successful young nobleman. While some young men like himself enjoyed gambling, dueling, and drinking to excess, Ignatius preferred to spend his free time composing poetry and courting young ladies.

The day finally arrived that changed Ignatius for the rest of his life. The French had laid siege to Pamplona and were determined to conquer it. Disgusted with the cowardly conduct of his men, who were ready to surrender, Ignatius convinced them to fight back. In defending the citadel from the French invaders, Ignatius performed great feats of bravery.

During the furious French artillery attack, Ignatius was struck by a cannon ball that shattered his right leg and seriously injured the left one. When Ignatius fell, so did the citadel he and his men tried in vain to defend from the French.

Ignatius was transported back to his childhood home of Loyola. His family brought in the finest physicians available at that time to treat his serious wounds. Not only was Ignatius in excruciating physical pain, but he knew that even if he were to survive, his career as a soldier and courtier was over. He would be deformed and lame for the remainder of his life. Because Ignatius's right leg had been poorly set by the army doctor, the surgeons had to break it again to place the bones in their right places. During this most agonizing operation, Ignatius did not utter a single cry or complaint, even though he was given nothing to deaden the pain.

Ignatius's condition grew worse. Late one night, he received the sacrament of anointing and prepared himself to die.

But death did not claim Ignatius. God had other plans for him. When he woke the following morning, he felt slightly better. Ignatius's life was out of danger. He still suffered great torment due to his injuries and many further procedures on his right leg, but he grew in health and strength as time passed.

Ignatius hoped to while away the many long hours of boredom during his recovery by escaping into novels of courtly romance and chivalrous adventure that were popular at the time. Since not a single such book could be found, he was offered some very different reading material. One book was about the life of Jesus. The other was an anthology of the lives of the saints. Before he was injured, Ignatius never could have imagined being interested in reading religious books.

He now found himself devouring page after page with great eagerness and joy. Ignatius was suddenly struck with the idea of imitating the lives of the great saints himself. "By God, if they were as I am, if they possessed the same nature as I do, why can I not do what they have done? To suffer for God, to do for Him what I have before now done and suffered only for my own vain and selfish interests — is that holiness not in itself a noble pursuit? Then I also can be holy, and it will be my own fault if I am not so."

It was in this way that God planted a seed in Ignatius. As the seed grew, Ignatius thought more and more about fully dedicating his life to serving God instead of himself.

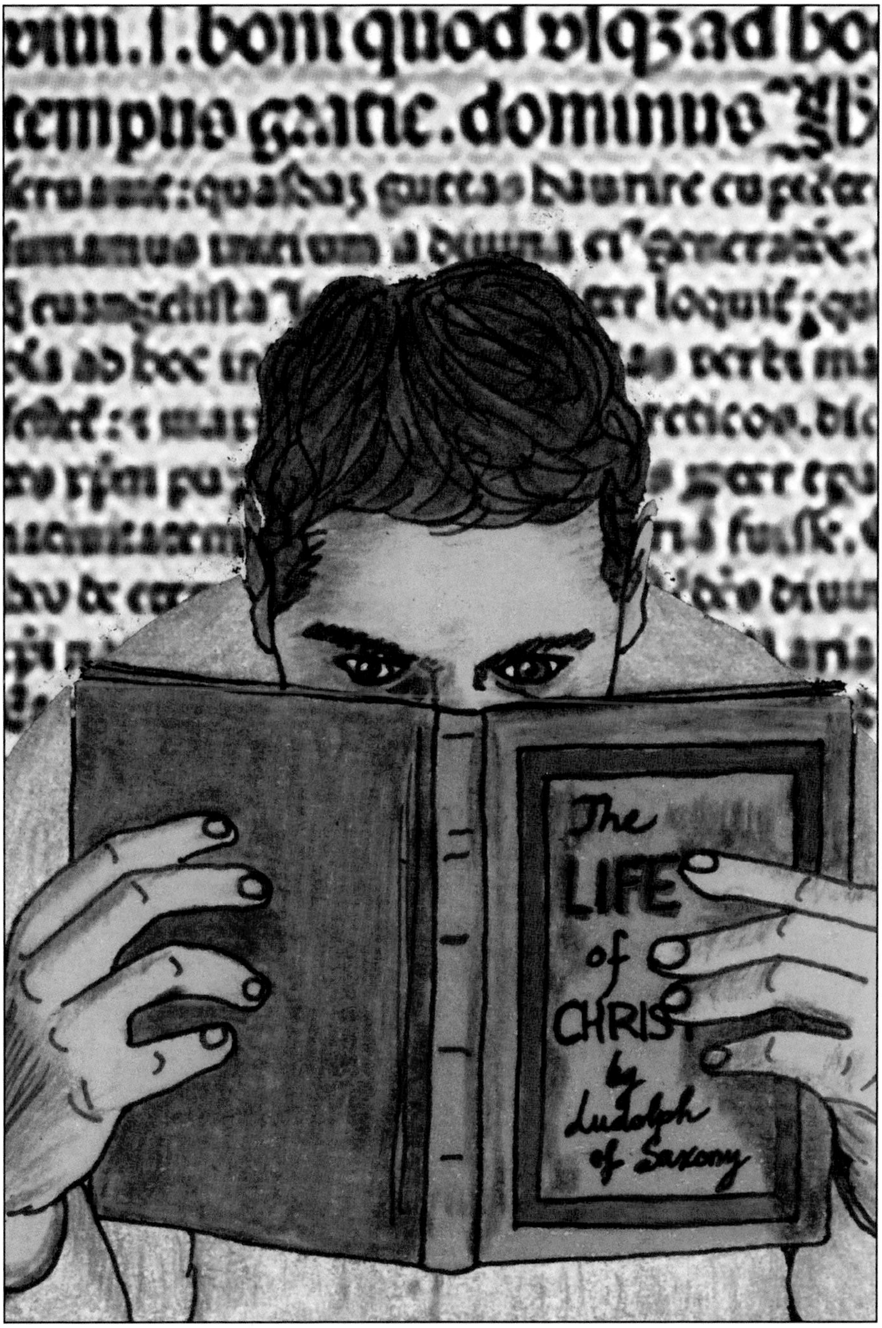
The
LIFE
of
CHRIS
by
Ludolph
of Saxony

At first he was afraid what people would think of him if he lived a religious life. His heart wavered back and forth, and many times, he yearned to experience the worldly pleasures of fame, fortune, and women again. In time, Ignatius realized that he felt perfect peace and happiness when he resolved to follow the Lord. The pleasures of the world had never made him feel this way.

When Ignatius's leg had recovered sufficient strength, he was determined to leave Loyola and begin his new life of holiness. Since he had been spending much of his time immersed in prayer and reflection on his sinful conduct of the past, he wanted very much to ask God for forgiveness and atone for his sins so that he could start anew. Ignatius felt that the best way to do this would be to make a pilgrimage and retreat in the holy monastery of Our Lady of Montserrat.

As Ignatius made preparations for the journey, he went to the Loyola stables to select a horse to ride. He was overwhelmed by the number of fine animals from which to choose. In Ignatius's fashionable youth, he never would have been seen riding anything other than the fastest, sleekest, costliest stallion. But appearances no longer mattered to Ignatius. He walked around the stables, not knowing which horse to choose, until a still, small voice stirred within him. He stopped in his tracks in front of an ordinary-looking brown horse. Ignatius somehow had a feeling this was the one for him. "*Hola, mi amigo*," Ignatius whispered as he stroked the horse's soft muzzle. "How would you like to be my companion on this very important journey? Would you do me that very great honor?"

Ignatius thought he must be imagining things, but it actually seemed as if the horse gave a brief nod of his head as he looked at him with huge, dark, intelligent eyes. *"Muy bien.* We shall be good traveling companions, you and I. I am going to call you Amigo," Ignatius said with satisfaction.

Ignatius saddled up Amigo and left Loyola. He and Amigo took the road leading to Montserrat, a mountain town in the northern part of Spain called Catalonia. As Ignatius rode, he contemplated the holy graces and favor the Mother of God had bestowed upon him. Suddenly, he found himself in the company of another traveler on horseback, who began to ride alongside him. This man was from a very different faith and culture.

Learning that Ignatius was on a pilgrimage to the monastery of Our Lady of Montserrat, the traveler began a discussion with Ignatius about the Mother of God. Ignatius tried calmly to answer the man's questions and set his false ideas straight, much the way a patient teacher would do with an ignorant pupil. What began as a friendly discussion, however, soon turned into a heated argument between the two men.

"I find the idea of your supposedly 'pure and holy Mother of God' almost laughable," the traveler mocked. "Your faith expects you to believe in fairy tales!" he sneered. "Just as ridiculous is the notion that Mary and her husband Joseph never had any more children after your so-called 'Savior' was born. How can anyone believe in such nonsense?" the man scoffed. Ignatius could no longer bear such blasphemy.

"I will not tolerate your bold impiety and shocking rudeness a moment longer, sir!" Ignatius spluttered in rage. "How DARE you talk about My Lady in such a disgraceful manner?" You see, despite his recent conversion to God's service, Ignatius was still very much a chivalrous knight at heart.

Realizing he had gone too far, the traveler spurred his horse and rode off at a full gallop, leaving Ignatius and Amigo behind in the dust. This was the final straw for Ignatius, whose wrath was now fully awakened. His immediate impulse was to avenge these insults to His Lady, the Holy Mother of God. "By all that is holy, am I not bound to defend her honor? What kind of sniveling coward would I be to accept such uncouth behavior and blasphemy from any man, let alone *this* one?" Ignatius touched the cold steel of the long sword he carried by his side. His fingers itched to wield it against the neck of this unworthy scoundrel.

"He will rue the day he blasphemed against My Lady!" Ignatius shouted. Amigo jerked nervously at this outburst.

After riding in silence for a few minutes, Ignatius suddenly pulled up hard on Amigo's reins, causing him to come to an abrupt stop. It was as if a lightning bolt hit Ignatius.

"Wait! Am I looking at this situation as a follower of Christ *should*?" he wondered aloud. "Amigo, what should I do? Should the punishment of the guilty perhaps be placed in the hands of God and not my own? I am thoroughly confused!" Amigo simply waited in peaceful silence.

Ignatius closed his eyes and poured out a spontaneous prayer from his heart. "Dear Father in Heaven, if it be your will that I kill this traveler for his blasphemy, let my Amigo follow him down the wide, smooth road that leads to the village where he is headed. If it be your will instead that I should let the man live, let Amigo take the narrow, stony, steep path that leads to the mountain. Forgive me, Lord, but I do not trust myself to make the right decision."

Amigo was shocked when he heard Ignatius's prayer. How could *he* possibly decide such a question? If Amigo took the easy road to the village, a man would be murdered. If he took the harder, narrow path, the man would live. No human had ever expected him to do anything like this ever before. Amigo stood rooted to the spot and gave Ignatius an angry snort. "I desperately need your help, *mi amigo*," Ignatius murmured, as he stroked the horse's velvety brown ears. He then placed Amigo's reins on the horse's neck, bowed his head, and waited.

As Amigo stood silently, it was as if a peaceful, soothing voice was whispering in his ears. It felt like the softest summer breeze. He closed his eyes and let the gentle voice sweep over him. Amigo gave a shuddering sigh that rippled through his entire body—Ignatius could feel it. All of a sudden, the horse knew what he must do.

Amigo started up the narrow, rocky path that led to the mountain. The traveler's life was spared. Ignatius wept with relief and hugged Amigo's neck in gratitude. "I can never repay you for your help, my wise friend. I am certain that the Lord, touched with compassion for my blind ignorance, gave you the wisdom to help me avoid committing a terrible sin I always would have had cause to regret." Amigo slowly swished his tail back and forth, as if to say, "Glad I could help."

After Ignatius and Amigo arrived at the monastery of Our Lady of Montserrat, Ignatius changed into a simple tunic of rough cloth and sandals and began his spiritual retreat. Never again would he wear the fine clothes of courtier.

Within the monastery's holy walls, Ignatius spent many hours in prayer and reflection before the miraculous Black Madonna, *la Moreneta*. It was there at His Lady's feet that Ignatius lay down his sword. From that day forward, he would be a man of peace, not violence.

In preparation for his confession, Ignatius thought long and hard about the gravest and most humiliating faults of his past life. "Teach me to serve you as you deserve, Lord," he prayed over and over again. Ignatius asked humbly to be forgiven of his sins.

During his many days spent in prayer, Ignatius gave thanks to God for his great love and begged to be granted the grace to understand more and more the way

God was working in his life. As he reviewed his conduct, his mind returned again and again to the incident on the road with the traveler, and how close he came to taking the man's life, had it not been for his wise and special horse, Amigo.

"How far I am from truly following in the way of the Lord!" Ignatius lamented. "How is it possible that I could become so enraged by this man's ignorance that I would even *consider* taking his life? That is the province of God alone! What an arrogant, egotistical sinner I am! How could I have considered myself even a little bit holy? I feel a much greater debt of gratitude to my Amigo than I even thought possible."

Ignatius went out to the stables to pay Amigo a visit. He stroked the horse's long, velvety muzzle as he spoke softly to him. "*Muchas, muchas gracias, mi querido amigo,*" Ignatius murmured. "Thank you for being the Lord's willing instrument for my benefit. Truly, you are such a wonder of God's creation! With His grace, I hope to be as wise as you one day," Ignatius laughed.

In time, Ignatius did grow wiser and closer to God. He learned that a person's life and attitude can be changed with God's help, but change takes time. It does not happen overnight. In the coming years of his life, Ignatius became well known for his holiness, but he often thought about the time his wise horse saved him from committing murder. The memory helped him to remain humble.

Often we are tempted to act impulsively and out of anger, if we do not stop to reflect on God's will. Like Ignatius, we will come to a crossroads many times in our lives, not knowing the right decision to make. Even though the right path may be narrow and hard to travel, God will find a way to help us, if we ask Him to lead us. As Ignatius experienced, God's help might even come from a most unexpected source!

Afterword

This little-known story about Saint Ignatius of Loyola (1491-1556) and his horse is based on fact. A short account of the episode is actually found within the pages of the saint's autobiography, which he dictated near the end of his life. Furthermore, it is included and elaborated on by many of Ignatius's early biographers.

During the latter part of his life, Ignatius was renowned as the influential founder of the Society of Jesus, or Jesuit order. He was regarded as a master of spiritual discernment and greatly admired for his holy wisdom. Even after five centuries, people still pray using his Daily Examen for self-reflection and live by Ignatius's philosophy of finding God in all things.

I have always been impressed by Ignatius's inclusion of this event in the telling of his life story. When one reads the *Autobiography*, it is quite evident that he left out a great deal. Why, then, did Ignatius choose to include this particular incident that occurred during the early days of his conversion? The fact that he very nearly murdered a man whose opinion he disliked, while believing himself already converted to living a life of God, is at least somewhat disturbing and most decidedly unsaintly. He could have simply omitted it from his autobiography, because this behavior makes him look hypocritical, misguided, and sinful. So why didn't he?

Saint Ignatius of Loyola, Circa1620, Peter Paul Rubens, public domain

Ignatius had the humility and honesty to admit to his behavior, even though he knew it didn't make him look good. No doubt he also found the experience had much to teach others, and therefore, it was worth sharing: beware of false pride; while change is possible, it is not easy, nor does it happen quickly; God will send us the help we need, even in the most unlikely of sources; even a saint may begin his journey to holiness as a foolish sinner; anger and impulsivity lead to sin, while reflection and prayer are key in knowing God's will; although taking the narrow path is more difficult, with God's help, it is possible to follow it, and ultimately, it is the most worthwhile.

The Virgin of Montserrat inspired Ignatius to be a man of peace.

St. Ignatius Loyola's Prayer for Generosity

Lord, teach me to be generous.
Teach me to serve you as you deserve;
To give and not to count the cost;
To fight and not to heed the wounds;
To toil and not to seek for rest;
To work and not to ask for reward,
Except that of knowing that I am doing Your will.
Amen.

About the Author

Hayley Medeiros is an artist and writer who lives in Scottsdale, Arizona. *Ignatius of Loyola and His Wise Horse* is her third picture book for children. She is also the author and illustrator of *Emmylou Finds Her Voice* and *Saint John Bosco and His Big Gray Dog*, both published by Caritas Press.

CARITAS PRESS

Other books by Hayley Medeiros

Saint John Bosco and His Big Gray Dog

It is hard to believe that anyone would have ever wanted to hurt good Father John Bosco. He helped so many people. But there were times when his life was in danger. During those times, a very special guardian would appear to protect him. In this way, God saved the holy priest from harm so he could complete his mission and help children come to know God.

Emmylou Finds Her Voice

A heartfelt tale of a hen with an unusual gift -- a talent for singing that brings scornful criticism from her envious peers. Emmylou rises above the bullying and even helps another hen to embrace her own beautiful differences.

CHILDREN'S BOOKS FROM CARITAS PRESS

ORDER AT CARITASPRESS.ORG OR AMAZON

ARCHANGELA'S HORSE
Archangela comes to understand God's will when her beloved and loyal horse refuses to take her where she wants to go.
By Sherry Boas

ARABEL'S LAMB
A young girl's compassion is tested to the limits in this gripping tale about love and sacrifice. Loosely based on the legend of St. George and the Dragon. By Sherry Boas

BILLOWTAIL
Little creatures on a big adventure in medieval Spain! 220-page Novel. By Sherry Boas

MIRACULOUS ME
A mother and father dream of the future as they celebrate the precious gift of life, the baby who is about to arrive. What will the days of her life hold? By Ruth Pendergast Sissel & Tina Tolliver Matney

BARNYARD BLISS
All of creation rejoices as word of the baby owlet spreads throughout the farm from one animal to the next. By Ruth Pendergast Sissel & Tina Tolliver Matney

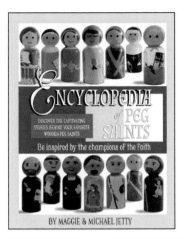

ENCYCLOPEDIA OF PEG SAINTS

Get to know 36 saints in an engaging and easy to "absorb" format, centered around colorful hand-painted peg dolls collected and cherished by Catholic kids everywhere. By Maggie & Michael Jetty

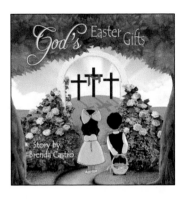

GOD'S EASTER GIFTS

A very special Easter egg hunt shows brother and sister, Pablo and Bella, that there's much more to Easter than candy and toys. By Brenda Castro

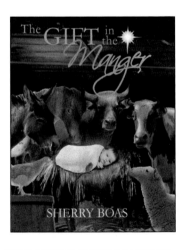

THE GIFT IN THE MANGER

When their feeding trough ends up serving as a bed for a tiny baby, the animals get a glimpse into God's loving plan to save the world. Like every one of us, each of the animals gathered around the manger has a struggle to overcome. They, like us, find the answer in Jesus, the only one who can fix our brokenness, heal our imperfections and give us the gift that makes us whole – the gift of Himself. By Sherry Boas

JACKIE'S SPECIAL HALLOWEEN

Sister and brother duo Bella and Pablo return in this delightful story about the true meaning of Halloween. Author Brenda Castro captures young imaginations and shows them the truth and beauty of the Faith, just as she does in her acclaimed debut work, God's Easter Gifts, a story about the two siblings finding the true meaning of Easter.
By Brenda Castro

Books for Mom & Dad

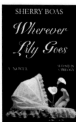
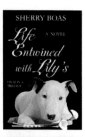

THE LILY SERIES BY SHERRY BOAS
Until Lily
Wherever Lily Goes
Life Entwined with Lily's
The Things Lily Knew
Things Unknown to Lily
A Little Like Lily

"...You will be entranced, you will experience the joys and sorrows of the characters, you will cry, and you will not be able to put Lily down."
– Dr. Jeff Mirus of CatholicCulture.org

The transforming power of love is at the heart of Sherry Boas' poignant series about the people whose lives are moved by a woman with Down syndrome. Lily's story is told with such brutal yet touching honesty, it will have you laughing one minute and reduced to tears the next.

WING TIP
A Novel

Dante De Luz's steel was forged in his youth, in the crucible of harsh losses and triumphant love. But that steel gets tested like never before as his mother's deathbed confession reveals something startling about his father and presents the young Catholic priest with the toughest challenge of his life, with stakes that couldn't get any higher.

"Aside from death and taxes, here's one more thing that is certain in this life: Sherry Boas' Wing Tip, will be a classic of Catholic literature. Magnificentread, highly recommended."

Robert Curtis,
The Catholic Sun

Rosary meditations for everyone in the family

Dads
Moms
Children
Teens
Grandparents
Altar Servers

Special full-color Gift Edition and Journal for Mom

Laughter of Angels
By Sherry Boas

New York City journalist Verdi Leoni discovers that death looms near for the scavenger who rescued her from a garbage dump when she was a baby. So Verdi quits her job at the newspaper and returns to her native China to take care of the ailing woman. But there is someone else in Shanghai who needs Verdi even more—someone who is not so easy to love. It takes all the strength Verdi can muster to care for the caustic old man, who holds the power—but no desire—to bind the wound she harbors in the depths of her soul. With the unfolding of a number of staggering revelations, Verdi begins to understand that nothing she thought she knew can be taken for granted, not even the story of her own life.

ORDER AT CARITASPRESS.ORG OR AMAZON

Made in the USA
Columbia, SC
11 April 2021

35989445R00018